KS2
Success

10-MINUTE TESTS

English

Alison Head

Sample page

clear instructional text

topic being covered

test number for quick reference

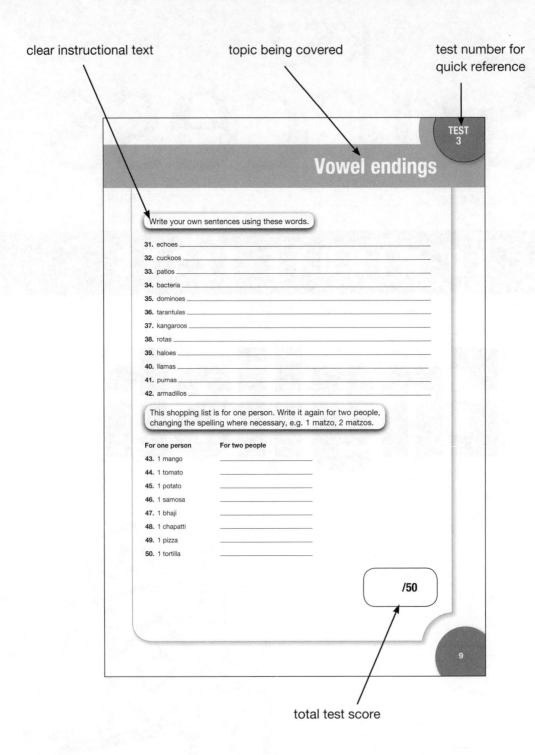

TEST 3

Vowel endings

Write your own sentences using these words.

31. echoes _____
32. cuckoos _____
33. patios _____
34. bacteria _____
35. dominoes _____
36. tarantulas _____
37. kangaroos _____
38. rotas _____
39. haloes _____
40. llamas _____
41. pumas _____
42. armadillos _____

This shopping list is for one person. Write it again for two people, changing the spelling where necessary, e.g. 1 matzo, 2 matzos.

For one person	For two people
43. 1 mango	_____
44. 1 tomato	_____
45. 1 potato	_____
46. 1 samosa	_____
47. 1 bhaji	_____
48. 1 chapatti	_____
49. 1 pizza	_____
50. 1 tortilla	_____

/50

9

total test score

Contents

Nouns

1–16. Sort the nouns from the box into the appropriate columns in the table below.

herd	Sally	Africa	fear	swarm	bravery
box	crowd	Amy	joy	table	
mountain	Wednesday	car	flock	excitement	

Common nouns	Proper nouns	Collective nouns	Abstract nouns

17–28. Now add three of your own nouns for each noun type.

Common nouns	Proper nouns	Collective nouns	Abstract nouns
17.	20.	23.	26.
18.	21.	24.	27.
19.	22.	25.	28.

Underline all of the nouns in each sentence.

29. Jane's happiness was written all over her face.

30. Max's understanding of symmetry is impressive.

31. The little girl's happy smile was lovely to see.

32. I took a bunch of flowers to school for Mrs Henry.

33. The man drove his car carefully through the snow.

34. London looked beautiful lit up in the moonlight.

35. I will always remember the man's kindness.

36. Last Friday it rained all day.

37. A flock of geese flew over the river.

38. Carrie blew out the candles and made a wish.

Nouns

Write your own sentences using these nouns.

39. love _____

40. April _____

41. swarm _____

42. Friday _____

43. peace _____

44. company _____

45. examination _____

46. jealousy _____

47. holiday _____

48. chalk _____

49. floor _____

50. valley _____

/50

Plurals

Write the plurals of these nouns.

1. church _____

2. party _____

3. wish _____

4. box _____

5. tree _____

6. game _____

7. foot _____

8. journey _____

9. puppy _____

10. donkey _____

11. bubble _____

12. gas _____

13. wolf _____

14. city _____

15. trolley _____

16. watch _____

17. tooth _____

18. child _____

19. calf _____

20. mouse _____

21. sky _____

22. person _____

23. pitch _____

24. man _____

25–30. Circle six words in the box that remain the same whether singular or plural.

crate	salmon	sheep	library
wolf	deer	match	aircraft
tuna	boat	species	key	tree

Plurals

Write these sentences again, making the bold singular nouns plural.

31. The girl put the **book** in her bag.

_____

32. The **lady** nibbled at the cucumber sandwiches.

_____

33. Faith decided to tidy the **bedroom**.

_____

34. Dad cleaned the **window**.

_____

35. Polly keeps the **necklace** in her jewellery box.

_____

36. Simon polished the **apple** in the fruit bowl.

_____

37. We caught a **trout** in the river.

_____

38. The **man** watched the television.

_____

39. The **bird** roosted in the **tree**.

_____

40. The **child** ate the **biscuit** greedily.

_____

/40

Vowel endings

Complete each word with the correct vowel ending.

1. phot_____

2. past_____

3. sk_____

4. tut_____

5. spaghett_____

6. log_____

7. pian_____

8. fiest_____

9. iglo_____

10. disc_____

11. koal_____

12. Russi_____

13. cell_____

14. sof_____

15. camer_____

16. yoy_____

17. kiw_____

18. umbrell_____

19. em_____

20. corg_____

Tick the correct plural form for each singular word.

21. area	areaes	☐	areas	☐
22. hero	heroes	☐	heros	☐
23. video	videos	☐	videoes	☐
24. tattoo	tattooes	☐	tattoos	☐
25. radio	radios	☐	radioes	☐
26. stereo	stereoes	☐	stereos	☐
27. disco	discos	☐	discoes	☐
28. zoo	zooes	☐	zoos	☐
29. solo	solos	☐	soloes	☐
30. photo	photos	☐	photoes	☐

Vowel endings

Write your own sentences using these words.

31. echoes _____

32. cuckoos _____

33. patios _____

34. bacteria _____

35. dominoes _____

36. tarantulas _____

37. kangaroos _____

38. rotas _____

39. haloes _____

40. llamas _____

41. pumas _____

42. armadillos _____

This shopping list is for one person. Write it again for two people, changing the spelling where necessary, e.g. 1 matzo, 2 matzos.

For one person	For two people
43. 1 mango	_____
44. 1 tomato	_____
45. 1 potato	_____
46. 1 samosa	_____
47. 1 bhaji	_____
48. 1 chapatti	_____
49. 1 pizza	_____
50. 1 tortilla	_____

/50

Prefixes

Choose a prefix from the box to add to each word.

auto	bi	trans	tele	circum

1. _____ + pilot = _____

2. _____ + vision = _____

3. _____ + plant = _____

4. _____ + form = _____

5. _____ + biography = _____

6. _____ + phone = _____

7. _____ + stance = _____

8. _____ + cycle = _____

9. _____ + scope = _____

10. _____ + navigate = _____

Join each word to the correct definition.

11. transatlantic   happening every two months

12. automatic   to move from one thing to another

13. television   a device operating under its own power

14. biennial   the ability to communicate without speaking

15. transfer   able to act or move by itself

16. automaton   on or from the other side of the Atlantic Ocean

17. telepathy   to move something from one place to another

18. biped   process of creating an image on a distant screen

19. transport   happening every two years

20. bimonthly   an animal with two feet

Prefixes

Circle the correct word in each pair.

21. imcredible   incredible   22. imresistible   irresistible

23. irregular   inregular   24. inproper   improper

25. indecent   ildecent   26. inpolite   impolite

27. iraccurate   inaccurate   28. inresponsible   irresponsible

29. impossible   inpossible   30. ilpatient   impatient

31. import   inport   32. immature   inmature

33. inreversible   irreversible   34. impose   inpose

35. inlegal   illegal   36. incapable   imcapable

37. indicate   imdicate   38. inrelevant   irrelevant

39. inpulse   impulse   40. inhabit   imhabit

Write a short story including these words. You can use them in any order. Read each word carefully before you begin.

41–45.

protect	improve	provide
produce	information	

_____

_____

_____

_____

_____

_____

_____

/45

Word roots

1–18. Colour in the words which share the same root. Use a different colour for each root.

act   government   operate   given   disapprove

cooperate   action   govern   pass   passenger

forgiveness   approval   prove   give

actor   passage   operator   governor

> Write a word that shares the same bold root as each of these words. Do not use plural forms of the root word. Remember, to make your new word you can either add a **prefix** or a **suffix** to the bold root.

19. childhood _____

20. electrician _____

21. publicity _____

22. discover**y** _____

23. heroism _____

24. painkiller _____

25. lightning _____

26. package _____

27. enjoyment _____

28. depress**ion** _____

29. hopeless _____

30. mistake**n** _____

Word roots

31. **usual**ly   _____

32. **develop**ing   _____

33. im**prison**ment   _____

34. ac**count**   _____

35. **favour**able   _____

36. **music**ian   _____

37. **assist**ance   _____

38. **agree**able   _____

39. **medic**ation   _____

40. re**call**   _____

41. **sign**al   _____

42. dis**interest**   _____

43. **infect**ious   _____

44. **clear**ance   _____

45. **disturb**ance   _____

46. **relax**ation   _____

47. **change**able   _____

48. **port**able   _____

49. **hand**icraft   _____

50. al**one**   _____

/50

Idioms

Complete these well-known idioms.

1. Don't count your chickens _____ they've hatched.

2. You shouldn't make a mountain out of a _____.

3. Let sleeping dogs _____.

4. Birds of a feather _____.

5. A leopard can't change its _____.

6. A stitch in time saves _____.

7. His bark is worse than his _____.

8. You have bitten off _____.

9. She got out of _____ on the wrong side.

10. A chain is no stronger than its _____ link.

11. Don't put all your eggs in one _____.

12. Between a rock and a _____ place.

13. _____ wasn't built in a day.

14. It's an ill _____ that blows no good.

15. Don't cry over _____ milk.

16. People who live in glass houses shouldn't throw _____.

17. A bad workman blames his _____.

18. Take a leaf out of his _____.

19. A _____ for your thoughts.

20. You're barking up the wrong _____.

Idioms

Write what each of these idioms means.

21. An apple a day keeps the doctor away.

_____

22. Keep your nose to the grindstone.

_____

23. Walk a mile in my shoes.

_____

24. Out of the frying pan, into the fire.

_____

25. Raining cats and dogs.

_____

26. Looking daggers at someone.

_____

27. Every cloud has a silver lining.

_____

28. If it isn't broken, don't fix it.

_____

29. You can't make a silk purse out of a sow's ear.

_____

30. Too many cooks spoil the broth.

_____

/30

Verbs

Write the past tense of each verb.

1. walk _____   2. speak _____

3. go _____   4. wish _____

5. sleep _____   6. am _____

7. buy _____   8. weep _____

9. give _____   10. lose _____

11. worry _____   12. find _____

13. whisper _____   14. live _____

15. sweep _____   16. save _____

17. cry _____   18. leap _____

19. think _____   20. run _____

Underline the correct verb to complete each sentence.

21. It was freezing when we [wake waked woke] up.

22. I always [feel felt feeled] sick when I am in the car.

23. Jack [saves save saved] his money so he could buy a new game.

24. If Samia [tried try tries] hard in her test, she will get a good mark.

25. Katie [catched catch caught] chickenpox from her little brother last year.

26. Mrs Brown [teached teaches taught] me guitar when I get home from school.

27. Mum [works worked working] in a sweet shop when she was younger.

28. Our pumpkins [grow grew growed] so big that we could not lift them.

29. If Mum [knew knowed knows] I have lost my coat, she would be furious!

30. My cousins [come comed came] to my party last week.

Verbs

Write these sentences again in the past tense.

31. Lauren always wins running races.

_____

32. Sam plays football, even when it is raining.

_____

33. Nakia's school uniform is navy blue.

_____

34. Dad enjoys visiting Spain because he can speak Spanish.

_____

35. The boys tidy their rooms every Saturday morning.

_____

36. My sister makes a terrible mess when she is looking for something.

_____

37. We visit the castle during our holiday.

_____

38. Bhavin often leaves his schoolbag on the bus by mistake.

_____

39. I usually get to school on time.

_____

40. I read loads of books during the summer holidays.

_____

/40

Adverbs

Complete the table by turning the adjectives into adverbs. The first one has been done for you.

Adjective	Adverb
kind	kindly
1. brave	
2. hopeful	
3. rapid	
4. colourful	
5. nervous	
6. rude	
7. late	
8. sure	
9. angry	
10. dainty	

Underline the adverb in each sentence.

11. The children greedily gobbled up the cake.

12. Jake stared dreamily out of the window.

13. Lara's hair stood out untidily all over her head.

14. The toddler wobbled unsteadily on her feet.

15. The school bell rang loudly to mark the end of the lesson.

16. Dad clapped proudly at the end of the play.

17. Leo finished his homework neatly so he would get top marks.

18. Suddenly, the wind blew the window open.

19. The flock of sheep grazed contentedly in the field.

20. Hundreds of stars twinkled brightly in the night sky.

Adverbs

Write these sentences again, adding a different adverb each time to alter its meaning. Try not to use the same adverb more than once on this page.

Katie walked _____ to school.

21. _____

22. _____

23. _____

24. _____

25. _____

Harry finished his homework _____.

26. _____

27. _____

28. _____

29. _____

30. _____

The old car drove _____ along the road.

31. _____

32. _____

33. _____

34. _____

35. _____

The children played _____ at the park.

36. _____

37. _____

38. _____

39. _____

40. _____

/40

More verbs

Underline the correct verb from the brackets to complete each sentence.

1. I [are am] too tired to finish my homework.

2. Rabbits [loves love] nibbling carrots.

3. "Why [was were] you late this morning?" asked Mr Malik.

4. Mum and Dad [watch watches] me play basketball every weekend.

5. Swallows [flies fly] south for the winter.

6. George always [laughs laugh] at the cartoons on TV.

7. Harmony [say says] she is coming to our house later.

8. I always [tries try] my best at school.

9. The boys [play plays] football in the back garden.

10. Eating fruit and vegetables [is are] good for you.

Add is, are, was or were to complete each sentence.

11. Claire _____ excited when she saw the pile of presents.

12. Anuja _____ going to a party this afternoon if she feels better.

13. We _____ the noisiest class in the school yesterday.

14. I will miss my friend because he _____ moving away.

15. Mum asked, "_____ you going to tidy your room today?"

16. Dad _____ angry when we broke the mirror.

17. Tom and Patrick _____ on their way here now.

18. Emily _____ afraid of the dark so she sleeps with a night light.

19. Dogs _____ great pets but they need a lot of attention.

20. We _____ just coming in when the telephone rang.

More verbs

Write these sentences again, correcting the errors.
Keep each sentence in the same tense as the original.

21. Do you know where Lisa were going?

_____

22. Is you looking forward to the theatre trip?

_____

23. Was you at ballet last week?

_____

24. The girls eats half of the pizza each.

_____

25. Robbie think he is the best writer in the class.

_____

26. My parents worries about us if we are late home.

_____

27. Mia's dog sleep on the end of her bed.

_____

28. Being active help to keep us healthy.

_____

29. Ben and Amy was sitting together in Science.

_____

30. If I wins the prize, I will share it with you.

_____

/30

Synonyms

Synonyms are words that have similar meanings.
Write a synonym for each of these words.

1. picture _____
2. lamp _____
3. conceal _____
4. snooze _____
5. lane _____
6. bravery _____
7. cold _____
8. large _____
9. hot _____
10. eat _____
11. build _____
12. hurry _____
13. push _____
14. buy _____
15. look _____
16. car _____
17. field _____
18. grumble _____
19. cloak _____
20. journey _____

Underline the appropriate word in the brackets to complete each sentence.

21. Pramila [crushed cracked] the egg into the cake mixture.

22. Dad found a [box crate] of matches and lit the candles on the cake.

23. The librarian [arranged planned] the books neatly on the shelf.

24. It was hot so Mark asked for a glass of [cold frosty] water.

25. We [soar fly] out to Greece on Thursday.

26. The joke was so funny, we laughed till we [mourned cried].

27. I [brushed swept] my hair before I went out.

28. Mum bought a [pipe tube] of stripy toothpaste.

29. Uncle Martin will [collect gather] us from school later.

30. I chose a [shiny glittery] red apple.

Synonyms

This story is full of boring words. Write it again, using at least one better synonym in each sentence. Some of the words you could change have been highlighted in bold.

31–40.

The weather was **bad** so the children couldn't go out to play. They were **very** bored. They looked out of the window at the rain **falling** down and wished it would stop. Then Meena had a **good** idea. "Let's play hide and seek", she **said**.

Carl **ran** off and hid behind the **heavy** curtain in the hallway. **Crouching** in the corner he saw a **small** doorway he had never seen before. He opened the door and **went** inside. It was **very dark** and he **saw** a tunnel ahead. "Meena will not be able to **find** me in here!" he thought.

_____

_____

_____

_____

_____

_____

_____

_____

_____

_____

_____

/40

Suffixes

Complete these word sums. Make sure you spell the completed words correctly!

1. hope + full   = _____

2. wish + full   = _____

3. colour + full   = _____

4. beauty + full   = _____

5. glee + full   = _____

6. joy + full   = _____

7. dread + full   = _____

8. rest + full   = _____

9. grace + full   = _____

10. plenty + full   = _____

11. use + full   = _____

12. pity + full   = _____

13. taste + full   = _____

14. delight + full   = _____

15. thought + full   = _____

16. hate + full   = _____

17. bash + full   = _____

18. truth + full   = _____

19. venge + full   = _____

20. boast + full   = _____

Suffixes

21–30. Circle 10 words in the box that you can add the suffix **ful** to.

pain	knowledge		ill	duty	spite
	strength	love	care		fear
bright	clever	deceit		spend	good
	bounty	gain	tear	clean	respect

Write your own sentences using these **ful** words.

31. harmful

_____

32. grateful

_____

33. awful

_____

34. useful

_____

35. helpful

_____

36. forgetful

_____

37. peaceful

_____

38. tuneful

_____

39. powerful

_____

40. cheerful

_____

/40

Adverb fun

Find the list of adverbs hidden in the wordsearch grid.

surely	madly	hurriedly
solidly	calmly	totally
freshly	tidily	rudely
politely	messily	reluctantly
playfully	horribly	cheaply
painfully	quickly	happily
softly	heavily	

r	e	l	u	c	t	a	n	t	l	y	d	u	e	p	q	x
r	i	e	d	m	s	v	o	i	g	l	s	f	y	r	w	t
h	j	t	s	s	o	l	i	d	l	y	r	k	j	v	e	p
m	b	g	u	l	a	t	p	i	o	w	d	h	n	a	z	a
k	h	u	r	r	i	e	d	l	y	r	c	v	e	t	q	i
c	q	m	e	e	u	v	k	y	t	x	n	e	s	a	c	n
m	a	d	l	y	z	d	b	a	e	i	o	u	y	f	h	f
b	r	l	y	y	y	t	e	p	q	e	c	b	q	n	e	u
o	v	g	m	e	s	s	i	l	y	o	v	e	q	r	a	l
s	o	f	t	l	y	t	w	a	y	u	r	f	u	a	p	l
d	l	y	o	m	y	e	s	y	h	o	r	r	i	b	l	y
e	a	v	t	n	u	y	a	f	t	e	l	e	c	b	y	p
c	h	e	a	v	i	l	y	u	p	q	e	s	k	q	r	a
h	i	l	l	a	e	i	t	l	v	g	m	h	l	i	n	k
m	e	n	l	s	t	p	o	l	i	t	e	l	y	f	o	x
r	a	n	y	r	u	p	l	y	t	e	x	y	u	v	k	y
q	m	e	n	u	v	a	e	i	o	u	m	h	l	t	s	p
a	r	m	o	r	i	h	a	p	p	y	a	r	r	i	v	e

Synonym fun

Write these synonyms in the grid. Start with the four-letter word.

4 letters

glad

5 letters

jolly
merry

6 letters

joyful

7 letters

content
pleased

8 letters

blissful
cheerful
thrilled

9 letters

delighted

Direct and reported speech

Decide whether each sentence contains direct or reported speech.
Tick the correct box.

1. "Hurry up or we'll be late!" urged Mum.   direct ☐   reported ☐

2. The little boy asked, "Can I have a balloon?"   direct ☐   reported ☐

3. The teacher explained it would be playtime soon.   direct ☐   reported ☐

4. "Let's play tennis," suggested Luke.   direct ☐   reported ☐

5. The dentist told me my teeth were perfect.   direct ☐   reported ☐

6. The old lady asked me to open the door for her.   direct ☐   reported ☐

7. "Stop it!" snapped Kiera.   direct ☐   reported ☐

8. "Would you like some more peas?" asked Dad.   direct ☐   reported ☐

9. Rashid told me that he had finished his book.   direct ☐   reported ☐

10. Susie complained that she was hungry.   direct ☐   reported ☐

11. "It's snowing!" said Evie, excitedly.   direct ☐   reported ☐

12. Greg muttered, "Go away!"   direct ☐   reported ☐

13. Amy asked Chris if he felt better.   direct ☐   reported ☐

14. "I'll see you later," said Dad, on his way out.   direct ☐   reported ☐

15. Miss Morgan told the class to settle down.   direct ☐   reported ☐

16. The little girl shouted, "I've won!"   direct ☐   reported ☐

17. Sam complained that the work was hard.   direct ☐   reported ☐

18. Max said he was learning to play chess.   direct ☐   reported ☐

19. "It's time for bed," said Mum, firmly.   direct ☐   reported ☐

20. "Is that a new top?" asked Mandy.   direct ☐   reported ☐

Direct and reported speech

Write these sentences again, as reported speech.

Example: "Hello," said Fred.
Answer: Fred said hello.

21. "Can we have a drink please?" asked the twins.

_____

22. "I love your picture Robbie," said Mr Parsons.

_____

23. "Get out of my room!" Maddie shouted at me.

_____

24. "I can't eat another thing!" said Dad, contentedly.

_____

25. "Have you seen the rainbow Matthew?" asked Abdul.

_____

26. "I need to buy eggs and milk," said Mum.

_____

27. "Don't forget your packed lunch," Gran reminded me.

_____

28. The man asked, "What time does the train leave?"

_____

29. "Henry VIII had six wives," explained Mr Cooper.

_____

30. "I'd like a book of stamps please," asked the woman.

_____

/30

Imperative

An imperative sentence makes a command, request or suggestion. Tick the imperative sentences.

1. "Come on!" said Stephen. ☐

2. Fold the paper in half. ☐

3. It is too late to play. ☐

4. Where has the teacher gone? ☐

5. Weigh out the ingredients carefully. ☐

6. Keep off the grass. ☐

7. Will it be playtime soon? ☐

8. Do not feed the pigeons. ☐

9. Post your letters here. ☐

10. The cake is in the oven. ☐

Underline the imperative verb in each sentence.

11. Find a safe place to cross the road.

12. Choose a place away from parked cars.

13. Do not cross near a bend in the road.

14. Wait at the kerb.

15. Look left and right.

16. Listen carefully for cars.

17. Wait for a gap in the traffic.

18. When it is safe, walk straight across the road.

19. Do not run.

20. Keep looking to the left and right as you cross.

Answer booklet: English 10-Minute Tests, age 9–10

Test 1
1–16.

Common nouns	Proper nouns	Collective nouns	Abstract nouns
box	Sally	herd	fear
mountain	Africa	swarm	bravery
table	Amy	crowd	joy
car	Wednesday	flock	excitement

17–28. Answers will vary.

29. Jane's happiness was written all over her face.
30. Max's understanding of symmetry is impressive.
31. The little girl's happy smile was lovely to see.
32. I took a bunch of flowers to school for Mrs Henry.
33. The man drove his car carefully through the snow.
34. London looked beautiful lit up in the moonlight.
35. I will always remember the man's kindness.
36. Last Friday it rained all day.
37. A flock of geese flew over the river.
38. Carrie blew out the candles and made a wish.

39–50. Sentences will vary.

Test 2
1. churches
2. parties
3. wishes
4. boxes
5. trees
6. games
7. feet
8. journeys
9. puppies
10. donkeys
11. bubbles
12. gas/gases
13. wolves
14. cities
15. trolleys
16. watches
17. teeth
18. children
19. calves
20. mice
21. skies
22. people
23. pitches
24. men

25–30. salmon, sheep, deer, aircraft, tuna, species
31. The girl put the books in her bag.
32. The ladies nibbled at the cucumber sandwiches.
33. Faith decided to tidy the bedrooms.
34. Dad cleaned the windows.
35. Polly keeps the necklaces in her jewellery box.
36. Simon polished the apples in the fruit bowl.
37. We caught some trout in the river.
38. The men watched the television.
39. The birds roosted in the trees.
40. The children ate the biscuits greedily.

Test 3
1. photo
2. pasta/paste
3. ski/ska
4. tutu
5. spaghetti
6. logo
7. piano
8. fiesta
9. igloo
10. disco
11. koala
12. Russia
13. cello
14. sofa
15. camera
16. yoyo
17. kiwi
18. umbrella
19. emu
20. corgi
21. areas
22. heroes
23. videos
24. tattoos
25. radios
26. stereos
27. discos
28. zoos
29. solos
30. photos

31–42. Sentences will vary.
43. 2 mangoes/mangos
44. 2 tomatoes
45. 2 potatoes
46. 2 samosas
47. 2 bhajis
48. 2 chapattis
49. 2 pizzas
50. 2 tortillas

Test 4
1. autopilot
2. television
3. transplant
4. transform
5. autobiography
6. telephone
7. circumstance
8. bicycle
9. telescope
10. circumnavigate
11. on or from the other side of the Atlantic Ocean
12. able to act or move by itself
13. process of creating an image on a distant screen
14. happening every two years
15. to move from one thing to another
16. a device operating under its own power
17. the ability to communicate without speaking
18. an animal with two feet
19. to move something from one place to another
20. happening every two months
21. incredible
22. irresistible
23. irregular
24. improper
25. indecent
26. impolite
27. inaccurate
28. irresponsible
29. impossible
30. impatient
31. import
32. immature
33. irreversible
34. impose
35. illegal
36. incapable
37. indicate
38. irrelevant
39. impulse
40. inhabit

41–45. Stories will vary.

Test 5
1–18. act, action, actor
government, govern, governor
operate, cooperate, operator
disapprove, approval, prove
given, forgiveness, give
passenger, pass, passage

Answers might include:
19. childlike
20. electrical
21. publication
22. covered
23. heroic
24. painful
25. delighted
26. unpack
27. joyful
28. pressure
29. hopeful
30. undertake
31. unusual
32. development
33. prisoner
34. discount
35. favourite
36. musical
37. assistant
38. agreement
39. medicine
40. calling
41. signature
42. interesting
43. infection
44. unclear
45. disturbing
46. relaxing
47. unchanged
48. export
49. handmade
50. lonely

Test 6
1. Don't count your chickens before they've hatched.
2. You shouldn't make a mountain out of a molehill.
3. Let sleeping dogs lie.
4. Birds of a feather flock together.
5. A leopard can't change its spots.
6. A stitch in time saves nine.
7. His bark is worse than his bite.
8. You have bitten off more than you can chew.
9. She got out of bed on the wrong side.
10. A chain is no stronger than its weakest link.
11. Don't put all your eggs in one basket.
12. Between a rock and a hard place.
13. Rome wasn't built in a day.
14. It's an ill wind that blows no good.
15. Don't cry over spilt milk.
16. People who live in glass houses shouldn't throw stones.
17. A bad workman blames his tools.
18. Take a leaf out of his book.
19. A penny for your thoughts.
20. You're barking up the wrong tree.
21. A healthy diet helps to keep you fit and well.
22. Keep working hard.
23. Look at things from my point of view before you judge me.
24. From one problem straight into another.
25. Pouring with rain.
26. Giving someone a hostile or threatening look.
27. A little good comes from every bad situation.
28. Don't change things that are working well.
29. You can't make a thing into something that it really isn't.
30. Too many people involved in something can create problems.

Test 7
1. walked
2. spoke
3. went
4. wished
5. slept
6. was
7. bought
8. wept
9. gave
10. lost
11. worried
12. found
13. whispered
14. lived
15. swept
16. saved
17. cried
18. leapt
19. thought
20. ran
21. woke
22. feel
23. saved
24. tries
25. caught
26. teaches
27. worked
28. grew
29. knew
30. came
31. Lauren always won running races.
32. Sam played football, even when it was raining.
33. Nakia's school uniform was navy blue.
34. Dad enjoyed visiting Spain because he could speak Spanish.

35. The boys tidied their rooms every Saturday morning.
36. My sister made a terrible mess when she was looking for something.
37. We visited the castle during our holiday.
38. Bhavin often left his schoolbag on the bus by mistake.
39. I usually got to school on time.
40. I read loads of books during the summer holidays.

Test 8

1. bravely
2. hopefully
3. rapidly
4. colourfully
5. nervously
6. rudely
7. lately
8. surely
9. angrily
10. daintily
11. The children <u>greedily</u> gobbled up the cake.
12. Jake stared <u>dreamily</u> out of the window.
13. Lara's hair stood out <u>untidily</u> all over her head.
14. The toddler wobbled <u>unsteadily</u> on her feet.
15. The school bell rang <u>loudly</u> to mark the end of the lesson.
16. Dad clapped <u>proudly</u> at the end of the play.
17. Leo finished his homework <u>neatly</u> so he would get top marks.
18. <u>Suddenly</u>, the wind blew the window open.
19. The flock of sheep grazed <u>contentedly</u> in the field.
20. Hundreds of stars twinkled <u>brightly</u> in the night sky.
21–40. Sentences will vary.

Test 9

1. am
2. love
3. were
4. watch
5. fly
6. laughs
7. says
8. try
9. play
10. is
11. Claire was excited when she saw the pile of presents.
12. Anuja is going to a party this afternoon if she feels better.
13. We were the noisiest class in the school yesterday.
14. I will miss my friend because he is moving away.
15. Mum asked, "Are/Were you going to tidy your room today?"
16. Dad was angry when we broke the mirror.
17. Tom and Patrick are on their way here now.
18. Emily is afraid of the dark so she sleeps with a night light.
19. Dogs are great pets but they need a lot of attention.
20. We were just coming in when the telephone rang.
21. Do you know where Lisa was going?

22. Are you looking forward to the theatre trip?
23. Were you at ballet last week?
24. The girls eat half of the pizza each.
25. Robbie thinks he is the best writer in the class.
26. My parents worry about us if we are late home.
27. Mia's dog sleeps on the end of her bed.
28. Being active helps to keep us healthy.
29. Ben and Amy were sitting together in Science.
30. If I win the prize, I will share it with you.

Test 10

1–20. Possible answers include:

1. image
2. light
3. hide
4. sleep
5. road
6. courage
7. chilly
8. huge
9. warm
10. gobble
11. construct
12. rush
13. shove
14. purchase
15. see
16. vehicle
17. meadow
18. complain
19. cape
20. trip
21. cracked
22. box
23. arranged
24. cold
25. fly
26. cried
27. brushed
28. tube
29. collect
30. shiny
31–40. Stories will vary.

Test 11

1. hopeful
2. wishful
3. colourful
4. beautiful
5. gleeful
6. joyful
7. dreadful
8. restful
9. graceful
10. plentiful
11. useful
12. pitiful
13. tasteful
14. delightful
15. thoughtful
16. hateful
17. bashful
18. truthful
19. vengeful
20. boastful
21–30. pain, duty, spite, care, fear, deceit, bounty, gain, tear, respect
31–40. Sentences will vary.

Test 12

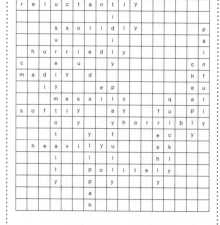

Test 13

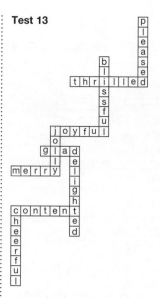

Test 14

Direct speech: 1, 2, 4, 7, 8, 11, 12, 14, 16, 19, 20

Reported speech: 3, 5, 6, 9, 10, 13, 15, 17, 18

21–30. Sentences may vary.
21. The twins asked for a drink.
22. Mr Parsons said he loved Robbie's picture.
23. Maddie shouted for me to get out of her room.
24. Dad said he couldn't eat another thing.
25. Abdul asked Matthew if he had seen the rainbow.
26. Mum said she needed to buy eggs and milk.
27. Gran reminded me to take my packed lunch.
28. The man asked what time the train leaves.
29. Mr Cooper explained that Henry VIII had six wives.
30. The woman asked for a book of stamps.

Test 15

1–10. Imperative sentences are: 1, 2 ,5 ,6, 8, 9
11. <u>Find</u> a safe place to cross the road.
12. <u>Choose</u> a place away from parked cars.
13. <u>Do not cross</u> near a bend in the road.
14. <u>Wait</u> at the kerb.
15. <u>Look</u> left and right.
16. <u>Listen</u> carefully for cars.
17. <u>Wait</u> for a gap in the traffic.
18. When it is safe, <u>walk</u> straight across the road.
19. <u>Do not run</u>.
20. <u>Keep looking</u> to the left and right as you cross.
21–30. Instructions will vary.

Test 16

1–10. Soft **c** words: receive, circle, scene, dancer, lance, ceiling, scissors, circus, accent, accident

11. fence **12.** circumference
13. receipt **14.** mince
15. lettuce **16.** face
17. hospice **18.** entice
19. pence **20.** sentence
21. A cygnet is a baby swan.
22. The vain girl was very conceited.
23. The man walked at such a fast pace that the dog couldn't keep up.
24. The law courts make sure that justice is done.
25. My favourite meal is chicken with rice.
26. My dad has a new job as a finance manager.
27. Liam has an apprenticeship at a local garage.
28. I am certain I have got all my sums right.
29. The medicine made Dawn feel much better.
30. We visited Mum at her office.
31–40. Sentences will vary.

Test 17

1. here **2.** hear
3. their **4.** there
5. too **6.** to
7. except **8.** accept
9. brake **10.** break
11. allowed **12.** aloud
13. led **14.** lead
15. lose **16.** loose
17. eight **18.** ate
19. sight **20.** site
21–40. Sentences will vary.

Test 18

1. mission **2.** magician
3. confusion **4.** competition
5. station **6.** pollution
7. session **8.** extension
9. optician **10.** explosion
11. possession **12.** completion
13. diction **14.** profession
15. emotion **16.** reduction
17. contribution **18.** mansion
19. education **20.** proportion
21. politician **22.** exclusion
23. fiction **24.** discussion
25. devotion **26.** attention
27. lotion **28.** distribution
29. position **30.** foundation
31. electrician **32.** direction
33. oppression **34.** transfusion
35. nation **36.** translation
37. repetition **38.** fraction
39. constitution **40.** promotion
41. petition **42.** deletion
43. occupation **44.** infusion
45. demonstration **46.** intuition
47. corrosion **48.** motion
49. opposition **50.** passion

Test 19

1–40. Answers might include:
1. cheap **2.** narrow
3. lose **4.** alive
5. decrease **6.** huge
7. sell **8.** short

9. mend **10.** close
11. low **12.** hard
13. awake **14.** pupil
15. woman **16.** child
17. light **18.** near
19. difficult **20.** early
21. ungrateful **22.** disobedient
23. incorrect **24.** improper
25. unhealthy **26.** illogical
27. impossible **28.** unrealistic
29. disorder **30.** impolite
31. The old woman was early for work.
32. In cold weather my rabbits spend a lot of time awake.
33. Mum checked to see if the old loaf of bread was stale.
34. The last time we went to Blackpool was in the summer.
35. The film was wonderful, so I was happy that I spent my own money on tickets.
36. The long skirt was covered in big flowers.
37. The squirrel ran up the tree with a big acorn in its mouth.
38. Unfortunately it started raining just before break time.
39. A beautiful fish swam quickly through the deep water.
40. I am too old to go on the little rides at the funfair.

Test 20

1. Tom was on the bus with Milly.
2. During the winter, we feed hay to the cattle.
3. What is your book about?
4. We climbed over the fallen tree that was blocking our path.
5. The hamster was asleep inside its little house.
6. The arrow flew through the air towards the target.
7. I wrote a letter to the newspaper about the new shopping centre.
8. The caterpillar had nibbled through the leaf.
9. A little mouse ran across the floor and into its hole.
10. The lovely bag is only on sale in the best shops.
11–20. Answers might include:
11. under **12.** after **13.** through
14. until **15.** for **16.** between
17. into **18.** above **19.** near
20. Inside
21. On top form.
22. Under the weather.
23. In for a penny, in for a pound.
24–25. Out of the frying pan, into the fire.
26. Between a rock and a hard place.
27. In hot water.
28. Make hay while the sun shines.
29. Going through the motions.
30. Age before beauty.
31–40. Descriptions will vary.

Test 21

1–35. Answers will vary.

Test 22

n	a	r	r	o	w								
o	i												
t		g			u	n	t	i	d	y			
h			h										
i	e	m	p	t	y					l			
n			a	s	m	a	l	l		o			
g	o		k	e						s			
	f		b	e	l	o	w			e			
	f			l									
s	u	b	t	r	a	c	t			d			
h	l		d							d			
r	o		o							i			
i		w	h	i	t	e		f	o	r	g	e	t
n			n							f			
k				d	i	v	i	d	e				
				c									
				u									
				l									
				t									

Test 23

1. crackle **2.** whistle
3. sniff **4.** rattle
5. smack **6.** clatter
7. drip **8.** whoosh
9. rip **10.** scrape

Test 24

1. Our dog dug up the bone and ate it.
2. Maisie was late home, so Dad went out to look for her.
3. The restaurant served us delicious pizza.
4. Habib is great at scoring goals, but he isn't so good at goalkeeping.
5. The boys were cold when they came in from playing in the snow.
6. My sister and I can watch a film after we get back from school.
7. Mum tried to catch the spider, but it scuttled under the sofa.
8. Claire has two kittens and loves taking care of them.
9. The balloon popped when it touched the holly bush.
10. Chris's shoes were too tight, so Mum bought him some more.
11. they **12.** it **13.** him
14. him **15.** I **16.** they
17. she **18.** we **19.** her
20. them
21. Kate hurt her ankle when she slipped off the kerb.
22. When the tree blew down it crushed our shed.
23. Max and Robin shared a cake because they could only afford one.
24. When my family arrived at the restaurant, the waiter took us to a table by the window.
25. Molly is the best dancer in our class because she has been dancing for many years.
26. Mr Welsh is a scary teacher because he shouts a lot.
27. Jessica and I were late for school because we took a wrong turning.

28. Uncle Pete took the TV back to the shop because it did not work.
29. Robert caught a crab after Mum showed him how to.
30. The children were fed up because they were tired of queuing for the ride.

Test 25

1. difference	2. boundary
3. business	4. separate
5. interest	6. literacy
7. library	8. category
9. offering	10. deafening
11. poisonous	12. frightening
13. jewellery	14. voluntary
15. desperate	16. interested
17. reference	18. memorable
19. opening	20. generally
21. carpet	22. company
23. definite	24. hospital
25. messenger	26. lottery
27. prepare	28. general
29. primary	30. easily
31. compromise	32. factory
33. family	34. Wednesday
35. extra	36. dictionary
37. conference	38. abandoned
39. description	40. abominable
41. freedom	42. flattery
43. animal	44. marvellous
45. formal	46. disinterest
47. original	48. generous
49. different	50. prosperous
51. heaven	52. library
53. elephant	54. familiar
55. predict	56. explanatory
57. miserable	58. literate
59. doctor	60. definitely

Test 26

1. taking	2. smiling
3. danced	4. loving
5. shaking	6. hopeful
7. lovely	8. shapely
9. sloping	10. waking
11. coped	12. lately
13. spiteful	14. joking
15. named	16. phoning
17. biting	18. tuned
19. dining	20. homely
21. toning	22. rating
23. lonely	24. tamed
25. fatal	26. noteworthy
27. spiky	28. traded
29. poked	30. moping

31–40. Sentences will vary.

Test 27

1–10. Correct sentences: 1, 4, 5, 6, 8.
11. "Don't wake Dad," whispered Mum.
12. "When will it stop raining?" wondered Jack.
13. "This isn't the one I wanted!" complained the man.
14. "You're wrong!" argued Sophie.
15. The teacher explained, "You need to measure carefully."
16. "Is this platform 4?" queried the woman.
17. Dad insisted, "You must eat your vegetables."
18. "Have you seen her dress?" gossiped the girls.
19. Will giggled, "That's so funny!"
20. "I'm thirsty," grumbled Elsa.
21–30. Possible answers include:
21. "David kicked me under the table!" moaned Robert.
22. "Can I tell you a secret?" whispered Fiona.
23. "There's a spider!" screeched Rachel.
24. Callum asked, "Is there any more pizza?"
25. "I've won!" gasped Mum.
26. Jane enquired, "Is the train on time?"
27. Joe argued, "That's not fair!"
28. "Light travels faster than sound," explained Mr Fitz.
29. "I hope your brother will be OK," worried Mum.
30. The man complained, "This soup is cold."
31–40. Answers will vary.

Test 28

1–10. Correct sentences: 1, 5, 7, 8, 9, 10
11. A train's passengers were forced to wait when it broke down.
12. The children's coats were hung up neatly in the cloakroom.
13. Many students' pictures were displayed on the wall.
14. Auntie Pat's car is bright pink.
15. The pigeons' heads bobbed back and forth as they walked about.
16. In my picture, all of the fairies' wings are sparkly.
17. The queen's crown was covered in diamonds.
18. The girls' noses were bright pink when they came in from the cold.
19. A little boy's shoes were on the wrong feet.
20. A dog's sense of smell is very good.
21–30. Answers will vary.

Test 29

1–10. Answers will vary.

Adjective	+er	+est
11–12. small	smaller	smallest
13–14. kind	kinder	kindest
15–16. brave	braver	bravest
17–18. big	bigger	biggest
19–20. bright	brighter	brightest
21–22. lovely	lovelier	loveliest
23–24. funny	funnier	funniest
25–26. rude	ruder	rudest
27–28. fit	fitter	fittest
29–30. young	younger	youngest

31–40. Answers will vary.
41–50. Answers will vary.

Test 30

1. The vase is broken because I dropped it.
2. The boys grabbed their bags and headed for school.
3. Although she was tired, Mum finished the ironing.
4. Mark was late, so he took the bus.
5. Mum went shopping while Dad took us to the cinema.
6. Because the car broke down, we had to call a taxi.
7. So he would remember his book, Sudip left himself a note.
8. After they had eaten their lunch, the children went outside to play.
9. I wanted to stay up late, but I was too tired.
10. We went to visit our aunt, but she was not in.
11. I am having a party because it is my birthday.
12. I read to Dad while he was cooking dinner.
13. Erin picked up the books and arranged them on the shelf.
14. The sun was shining, so we played in the garden.
15. Jayden shared his lunch although he was hungry.
16. Gemma likes netball but Marie prefers gymnastics.
17. The teacher was pleased because the class had worked well.
18. Because it was raining, the laundry got wet.
19. Despite her headache, Leah went to drama club.
20. Before crossing the road, the girls looked carefully both ways.
21–30. Answers may vary:
21. It was windy and a tree blew down.
22. We missed the bus, so we had to wait for the next one.
23. I looked for my phone and it was under my bed.
24. We clapped and cheered when our team scored a goal.
25. We looked at the stars when night fell.
26. I wanted strawberry ice-cream, but the shop only had vanilla.
27. Joe entered the competition and he won!
28. It was not raining although the sky was full of black clouds.
29. The woman sat down for a rest because her shopping bags were heavy.
30. I told her the secret because I trusted her.

Published by Letts Educational
An imprint of HarperCollins*Publishers*
77–85 Fulham Palace Road, London W6 8JB

ISBN 9781844197255

Text © Alison Head

Design and illustration © 2013 Letts Educational, an imprint of HarperCollins*Publishers*

Imperative

21–30. Write your own instructions for playing a favourite game. Write 10 sentences and use imperative verbs.

_____

_____

_____

_____

_____

_____

_____

_____

_____

_____

/30

Soft c

1–10. Circle the words in the box that contain a soft **c**.

receive	seen	sense	circle
scene	dancer	class	crate
calm	ceiling	cooker	
circus	cupboard	sent	accent
lance	accident	scissors	

Tick the correctly spelled word in each pair.

11. fence	☐	fense	☐
12. sircumference	☐	circumference	☐
13. receipt	☐	reseipt	☐
14. minse	☐	mince	☐
15. lettuce	☐	lettuse	☐
16. face	☐	fase	☐
17. hospise	☐	hospice	☐
18. entise	☐	entice	☐
19. pence	☐	pense	☐
20. sentense	☐	sentence	☐

Underline a soft c word in each sentence.

21. A cygnet is a baby swan.

22. The vain girl was very conceited.

23. The man walked at such a fast pace that the dog couldn't keep up.

24. The law courts make sure that justice is done.

25. My favourite meal is chicken with rice.

Soft *c*

26. My dad has a new job as a finance manager.

27. Liam has an apprenticeship at a local garage.

28. I am certain I have got all my sums right.

29. The medicine made Dawn feel much better.

30. We visited Mum at her office.

Write your own sentences using these words.

31. race _____

32. spicy _____

33. since _____

34. nice _____

35. centre _____

36. city _____

37. recipe _____

38. vaccine _____

39. space _____

40. voice _____

/40

Homophones

Homophones are words that sound the same but have different meanings. Circle the correct word in the brackets to complete each sentence.

1. "Come [here hear]," said Mrs Ross.

2. We could [here hear] fireworks in the distance.

3. The boys packed away [there their] PE kits.

4. Will [there their] be time to play later?

5. The little girl was [to too] short to reach the high shelf.

6. We walk [to too] school with our friends.

7. Everyone passed the test [except accept] Ali.

8. I hope the teacher will [except accept] my apology.

9. Dad had to [brake break] hard when a cat ran into the road.

10. The boys will [brake break] the window if their ball hits it.

11. I am not [allowed aloud] to play outside when it is dark.

12. Paddy loves to read [allowed aloud] to the class.

13. Our teacher [lead led] us around the art gallery.

14. The church roof is covered in [lead led].

15. If I [loose lose] my lunch money, I will have nothing to eat.

16. The cows got [loose lose] and wandered through the village.

17. There are [eight ate] children going on the school trip.

18. My sister [eight ate] the last piece of cake.

19. We caught [sight site] of the white cliffs of Dover.

20. It is not safe to play on a building [sight site].

Homophones

Write your own sentences using these homophones.

21. weather _____

22. whether _____

23. weight _____

24. wait _____

25. meet _____

26. meat _____

27. no _____

28. know _____

29. waste _____

30. waist _____

31. eye _____

32. I _____

33. past _____

34. passed _____

35. by _____

36. buy _____

37. rode _____

38. road _____

39. their _____

40. there _____

/40

More suffixes

Circle the correctly spelled word in each group.

1.	mition	mission	mician
2.	magician	magitian	magission
3.	confution	confussion	confusion
4.	competition	competission	competician
5.	station	stacian	stasion
6.	pollucian	pollution	pollusion
7.	session	sesion	setion
8.	extention	extencian	extension
9.	optition	optician	optission
10.	explosion	explotion	explossion
11.	possetion	possession	possesion
12.	completion	complecian	complesion
13.	diction	dictian	dicsion
14.	profecian	profesion	profession
15.	emotion	emocian	emosion
16.	reducian	reducsion	reduction
17.	contribution	contribusion	contribucian
18.	mantion	manssion	mansion
19.	educasion	educacian	education
20.	proporsion	proporcian	proportion

Add **cian**, **sion**, **ssion** or **tion** to complete each word.

21. politi_____

22. exclu_____

23. fic_____

24. discu_____

25. devo_____

More suffixes

26. atten_____

27. lo_____

28. distribu_____

29. posi_____

30. founda_____

31. electri_____

32. direc_____

33. oppre_____

34. transfu_____

35. na_____

36. transla_____

37. repeti_____

38. frac_____

39. constitu_____

40. promo_____

41. peti_____

42. dele_____

43. occupa_____

44. infu_____

45. demonstra_____

46. intui_____

47. corro_____

48. mo_____

49. opposi_____

50. pa_____

/50

Antonyms

An antonym is a word that has the opposite meaning to that of another word. Write antonyms for these words.

1. expensive _____
2. wide _____
3. find _____
4. dead _____
5. increase _____
6. tiny _____
7. buy _____
8. tall _____
9. break _____
10. open _____
11. high _____
12. soft _____
13. asleep _____
14. teacher _____
15. man _____
16. adult _____
17. dark _____
18. far _____
19. easy _____
20. late _____

Use a suitable prefix to make antonyms for these words.

21. _____ + grateful = _____
22. _____ + obedient = _____
23. _____ + correct = _____
24. _____ + proper = _____
25. _____ + healthy = _____
26. _____ + logical = _____

Antonyms

27. _____ + possible = _____

28. _____ + realistic = _____

29. _____ + order = _____

30. _____ + polite = _____

> Write each sentence again, replacing the bold words with their antonyms.

31. The **young man** was **late** for work.

_____

32. In **hot** weather my rabbits spend a lot of time **asleep**.

_____

33. Mum checked to see if the **new** loaf of bread was **fresh**.

_____

34. The **first** time we went to Blackpool was in the **winter**.

_____

35. The film was **awful**, so I was **unhappy** that I spent my own money on tickets.

_____

36. The **short** skirt was covered in **tiny** flowers.

_____

37. The squirrel ran **down** the tree with a **little** acorn in its mouth.

_____

38. **Fortunately** it **stopped** raining just before break time.

_____

39. An **ugly** fish swam **slowly** through the **shallow** water.

_____

40. I am too **young** to go on the **big** rides at the funfair.

_____

/40

Prepositions

Underline the prepositions in each sentence.
Some sentences have more than one.

1. Tom was on the bus with Milly.

2. During the winter, we feed hay to the cattle.

3. What is your book about?

4. We climbed over the fallen tree that was blocking our path.

5. The hamster was asleep inside its little house.

6. The arrow flew through the air towards the target.

7. I wrote a letter to the newspaper about the new shopping centre.

8. The caterpillar had nibbled through the leaf.

9. A little mouse ran across the floor and into its hole.

10. The lovely bag is only on sale in the best shops.

Add a suitable preposition to complete each sentence.

11. We sheltered from the rain _____ our umbrellas.

12. I have to do all of my homework _____ school.

13. On the way to the shops, we have to walk _____ a narrow alleyway.

14. I can't wait _____ it is my birthday.

15. Maria bought a new collar _____ her cat.

16. The letter b comes _____ a and c in the alphabet.

17. I paid all of my birthday money _____ my savings account.

18. My best friend lives in the flat _____ ours.

19. My teacher lets me sit _____ my friend in class.

20. _____ the envelope were tickets for the concert.

Prepositions

Add a preposition to each of these well-known phrases.

21. _____ top form.

22. _____ the weather.

23. _____ for a penny, in for a pound.

24–25. _____ of the frying pan, _____ the fire.

26. _____ a rock and a hard place.

27. _____ hot water.

28. Make hay _____ the sun shines.

29. Going _____ the motions.

30. Age _____ beauty.

31–40. Write a description of your journey to school, using prepositions. Write at least 10 sentences.

_____

_____

_____

_____

_____

_____

_____

_____

_____

_____

_____

/40

Onomatopoeia

Onomatopoeia is where words sound like the things they describe. Write a noun you associate with each of these onomatopoeic words.

1. hiss _____

2. buzz _____

3. bang _____

4. pop _____

5. sizzle _____

6. drip _____

7. sniff _____

8. howl _____

9. chuckle _____

10. slither _____

11. whoosh _____

12. clatter _____

13. crunch _____

14. click _____

15. squelch _____

16. squeak _____

17. thud _____

18. creak _____

Write onomatopoeic words to describe the noise these things make.

19. a parrot _____

20. a pile of tin cans falling over _____

Onomatopoeia

21. a bonfire　　　　　　　　　　　_____

22. stamping in a puddle　　　　　_____

23. speaking very quietly　　　　　_____

24. a twig breaking　　　　　　　_____

25. a window breaking　　　　　　_____

26–35. Choose one of these themes and write a poem about it, using as much onomatopoeia as you can. Your poem should be at least 10 lines long. Before you start, you may find it useful to create a word bank of onomatopoeic words for your chosen theme on a separate piece of paper.

- a snake slithering through dry grass
- a storm at sea
- a fireworks display

_____

_____

_____

_____

_____

_____

_____

_____

_____

_____

/35

Antonym fun

Find the antonyms of these words hidden in the wordsearch grid.

big	wide	something	day
come	on	buy	above
full	give	win	grow
up	add	multiply	remember
easy	black	tidy	quick

n	a	r	r	o	w	r	e	l	u	c	t	a	n	t
o	i	i	e	d	m	s	v	o	i	g	l	s	f	d
t	v	g	r	u	n	t	i	d	y	r	i	b	l	y
h	k	a	h	h	j	t	s	s	o	l	i	d	l	r
i	e	m	p	t	y	u	a	t	p	i	o	w	d	h
n	t	w	a	a	s	m	a	l	l	r	f	u	a	p
g	o	k	q	k	e	v	k	y	o	v	e	t	q	i
z	f	s	b	e	l	o	w	x	s	b	r	a	y	e
a	f	i	l	y	l	h	o	r	e	e	c	b	y	p
s	u	b	t	r	a	c	t	p	q	e	c	b	q	n
h	l	w	d	n	l	s	t	p	d	s	k	q	r	a
r	z	o	o	e	a	v	t	n	i	m	h	l	i	n
i	q	r	w	h	i	t	e	g	f	o	r	g	e	t
n	u	d	n	c	h	e	a	v	f	e	s	a	c	n
k	z	d	b	a	e	d	i	v	i	d	e	n	a	z
q	m	e	n	u	v	a	e	i	c	u	m	h	l	t
c	h	e	a	v	i	l	y	u	u	q	e	s	k	q
r	a	n	y	r	u	p	l	y	l	e	x	y	u	v
a	r	m	o	r	i	h	a	p	t	y	a	r	r	i

Fun with onomatopoeia

Unscramble the onomatopoeic words.

1. ckelcra _____ like a bonfire

2. istwhle _____ like a referee

3. iffsn _____ if you have a cold

4. ralett _____ a kind of snake

5. macsk _____ like a ball hitting a wall

6. latcter _____ like a ladder falling over

7. ridp _____ like raindrops

8. shoohw _____ up like a rocket

9. pri _____ like paper

10. scrpea _____ like removing ice from a windscreen

Pronouns

Underline the pronoun in each sentence.

1. Our dog dug up the bone and ate it.

2. Maisie was late home, so Dad went out to look for her.

3. The restaurant served us delicious pizza.

4. Habib is great at scoring goals, but he isn't so good at goalkeeping.

5. The boys were cold when they came in from playing in the snow.

6. My sister and I can watch a film after we get back from school.

7. Mum tried to catch the spider, but it scuttled under the sofa.

8. Claire has two kittens and loves taking care of them.

9. The balloon popped when it touched the holly bush.

10. Chris's shoes were too tight, so Mum bought him some more.

Choose the best pronoun from the brackets to complete each sentence.

11. The children missed some of their playtime because _____ were being too noisy. [it they us]

12. The cat saw a squirrel and chased _____ up a tree. [us her it]

13. I am going to Matthew's party, so I will buy _____ a present. [her us him]

14. My little brother is ill, so Dad took _____ to the doctor's. [him he you]

15. _____ love my bedroom because it has all my things in it. [He Her I]

16. My cousins can speak Spanish because _____ live in Spain.
    [we they them]

17. The lady ran down the street because _____ needed to catch the bus.
    [her he she]

18. My sister and I get into trouble if _____ don't keep our rooms tidy.
    [we you it]

19. It is Mum's birthday, so Dad bought _____ some flowers. [her he them]

20. The people had lots of shopping, so the assistant fetched _____ a trolley.
    [they them us]

Pronouns

Write these sentences again, replacing the bold words with a suitable pronoun.

21. Kate hurt her ankle when **Kate** slipped off the kerb.

_____

22. When the tree blew down **the tree** crushed our shed.

_____

23. Max and Robin shared a cake because **Max and Robin** could only afford one.

_____

24. When my family arrived at the restaurant, the waiter took **my family** to a table by the window.

_____

25. Molly is the best dancer in our class because **Molly** has been dancing for many years.

_____

26. Mr Welsh is a scary teacher because **Mr Welsh** shouts a lot.

_____

27. Jessica and I were late for school because **Jessica and I** took a wrong turning.

_____

28. Uncle Pete took the TV back to the shop because **the TV** did not work.

_____

29. Robert caught a crab after Mum showed **Robert** how to.

_____

30. The children were fed up because **the children** were tired of queuing for the ride.

_____

/30

Unstressed vowels

Underline the unstressed vowel in each word.

1. difference
2. boundary
3. business
4. separate
5. interest
6. literacy
7. library
8. category
9. offering
10. deafening
11. poisonous
12. frightening
13. jewellery
14. voluntary
15. desperate
16. interested
17. reference
18. memorable
19. opening
20. generally

Add the missing unstressed vowel to complete each word.

21. carp_____t
22. comp_____ny
23. def_____nite
24. hosp_____tal
25. mess_____nger
26. lott_____ry
27. pr_____pare
28. gen_____ral
29. prim_____ry
30. eas_____ly
31. compr_____mise
32. fact_____ry
33. fam_____ly
34. Wedn_____sday
35. extr_____
36. diction_____ry
37. conf_____rence
38. aband_____ned
39. d_____scription
40. abom_____nable

Unstressed vowels

Circle the correctly spelled word in each group.

41. freedum   freedom   freedem

42. flattery   flattory   flattary

43. anamal   anemal   animal

44. marvilous   marvellous   marvalous

45. formel   formul   formal

46. disintarest   disinterest   disinturest

47. origanal   origunal   original

48. generous   genarous   genorous

49. different   diffarent   diffurent

50. prosporous   prosperous   prosparous

51. heaven   heavan   heavun

52. librery   librory   library

53. elephant   eliphant   elophant

54. familier   familior   familiar

55. predict   pradict   prodict

56. explanatery   explanatory   explanatury

57. misarable   miserable   misorable

58. literate   litarate   litorate

59. docter   doctur   doctor

60. definately   definitely   definetely

/60

Modifying e

Complete these word sums by adding the suffixes.

1. take + ing = _____

2. smile + ing = _____

3. dance + ed = _____

4. love + ing = _____

5. shake + ing = _____

6. hope + ful = _____

7. love + ly = _____

8. shape + ly = _____

9. slope + ing = _____

10. wake + ing = _____

11. cope + ed = _____

12. late + ly = _____

13. spite + ful = _____

14. joke + ing = _____

15. name + ed = _____

16. phone + ing = _____

17. bite + ing = _____

18. tune + ed = _____

19. dine + ing = _____

20. home + ly = _____

Modifying e

Circle the correctly spelled word in each pair.

21. toneing   toning
22. rating   rateing
23. lonely   lonly
24. tamed   tameed
25. fateal   fatal
26. noteworthy   notworthy
27. spikey   spiky
28. tradeed   traded
29. poked   pokd
30. mopeing   moping

Write your own sentences using these words.

31. writing _____
32. making _____
33. safety _____
34. movement _____
35. closing _____
36. shiny _____
37. diving _____
38. timing _____
39. typed _____
40. baking _____

/40

Writing speech

Decide whether each sentence has the correct speech punctuation, then put a tick or a cross in the box at the end.

1. "It's time to tidy up your things," reminded Mum. ☐

2. "Dad complained, the car won't start." ☐

3. Can I get you some drinks? "asked the waitress." ☐

4. Bobby asked, "Why is the sky blue?" ☐

5. "Your tickets are booked now," confirmed the lady. ☐

6. "How about checking your spelling?" suggested Claire. ☐

7. "What were you doing in the hall? demanded Mr Turner. ☐

8. "Don't worry. It will be fine," comforted Grandma. ☐

9. "Come" in, said Auntie Beth, opening the door. ☐

10. "Go away!" snapped my sister, rudely." ☐

Add the speech punctuation to these sentences.

11. Don't wake Dad, whispered Mum.

12. When will it stop raining? wondered Jack.

13. This isn't the one I wanted! complained the man.

14. You're wrong! argued Sophie.

15. The teacher explained, You need to measure carefully.

16. Is this platform 4? queried the woman.

17. Dad insisted, You must eat your vegetables.

18. Have you seen her dress? gossiped the girls.

19. Will giggled, That's so funny!

20. I'm thirsty, grumbled Elsa.

Writing speech

Add an alternative to "said" to each sentence. Use the ideas in this test if you get stuck and try not to use the same word more than once.

21. "David kicked me under the table!" _____ Robert.

22. "Can I tell you a secret?" _____ Fiona.

23. "There's a spider!" _____ Rachel.

24. Callum _____, "Is there any more pizza?"

25. "I've won!" _____ Mum.

26. Jane _____, "Is the train on time?"

27. Joe _____, "That's not fair!"

28. "Light travels faster than sound," _____ Mr Fitz.

29. "I hope your brother will be OK," _____ Mum.

30. The man _____, "This soup is cold."

31–40. Write your own conversation between two characters, using the correct speech punctuation and avoiding the word "said" where possible.

_____

_____

_____

_____

_____

_____

_____

/40

Possessive apostrophes

Decide whether each sentence has the possessive apostrophe in the correct place, then put a tick or a cross in the box at the end.

1. A girl's story won the competition. ☐

2. The boys' toe was broken during the football match. ☐

3. The mens' briefcases were lined up on the train. ☐

4. The dogs' tail wagged frantically when he saw us. ☐

5. My hamster's fur feels soft when you stroke her. ☐

6. Brionys' hair is really long. ☐

7. My favourite book's pages were creased and torn. ☐

8. A squirrel's tail is long and bushy. ☐

9. Most cities' roads are very busy during rush hour. ☐

10. Three babies' prams were parked outside the shop. ☐

Add the possessive apostrophe to each sentence.

11. A trains passengers were forced to wait when it broke down.

12. The childrens coats were hung up neatly in the cloakroom.

13. Many students pictures were displayed on the wall.

14. Auntie Pats car is bright pink.

15. The pigeons heads bobbed back and forth as they walked about.

16. In my picture, all of the fairies wings are sparkly.

17. The queens crown was covered in diamonds.

18. The girls noses were bright pink when they came in from the cold.

19. A little boys shoes were on the wrong feet.

20. A dogs sense of smell is very good.

Possessive apostrophes

Think of sensible ways to end these sentences.

21. The lady's _____ .

22. The women's _____ .

23. Four cats' _____ .

24. A town's _____ .

25. The cars' _____ .

26. The companies' _____ .

27. The club's _____ .

28. Magazines' _____ .

29. Lucy's _____ .

30. The twins' _____ .

/30

Adjectives

Add a suitable adjective to each sentence.

1. A _____ butterfly fluttered from rose to rose.

2. The _____ kitten played with a ball of string.

3. We baked a _____ cake at school.

4. _____ snowflakes drifted to the ground.

5. A _____ boy rang the doorbell then ran away.

6. We organised a _____ birthday party for Sam.

7. Chloe was my _____ friend at school.

8. The toffee was _____ and _____.

9. A _____, _____ kite bobbed in the sky.

10. The _____ boy scored full marks in the test.

Complete the table by adding suffixes to the adjectives.

Adjective	+er	+est
11–12. small		
13–14. kind		
15–16. brave		
17–18. big		
19–20. bright		
21–22. lovely		
23–24. funny		
25–26. rude		
27–28. fit		
29–30. young		

Adjectives

31–40. Add suitable adjectives to this piece of text to create a spooky mood.

Connor walked cautiously up the _____ pathway towards the house.

_____ windows stared down at him, framed by _____

wooden shutters. He tried the _____ door, which creaked open on

_____ hinges.

Inside the house was totally _____. _____ curtains hung at

the windows and cobwebs covered the _____ wallpaper. A crooked flight of

stairs led up into _____ darkness. Connor was _____.

41–50. Write your own description of a theme park, using lots of powerful adjectives.

_____

_____

_____

_____

_____

_____

_____

_____

_____

_____

/50

Sentences

1. The vase is broken because I dropped it.

2. The boys grabbed their bags and headed for school.

3. Although she was tired, Mum finished the ironing.

4. Mark was late, so he took the bus.

5. Mum went shopping while Dad took us to the cinema.

6. Because the car broke down, we had to call a taxi.

7. So he would remember his book, Sudip left himself a note.

8. After they had eaten their lunch, the children went outside to play.

9. I wanted to stay up late, but I was too tired.

10. We went to visit our aunt, but she was not in.

Choose the best connective from the brackets to complete each sentence.

11. I am having a party _____ it is my birthday. [although so because]

12. I read to Dad _____ he was cooking dinner. [during while and]

13. Erin picked up the books _____ arranged them on the shelf. [and so but]

14. The sun was shining, _____ we played in the garden.
    [however although so]

15. Jayden shared his lunch _____ he was hungry. [because although but]

16. Gemma likes netball _____ Marie prefers gymnastics. [so because but]

17. The teacher was pleased _____ the class had worked well.
    [and so because]

18. _____ it was raining, the laundry got wet. [So Although Because]

19. _____ her headache, Leah went to drama club. [Despite Although Because]

20. _____ crossing the road, the girls looked carefully both ways.
    [After Before And]

Sentences

Write each pair of sentences again as one sentence, replacing the full stop with a suitable connective.

21. It was windy. A tree blew down.

_____

22. We missed the bus. We had to wait for the next one.

_____

23. I looked for my phone. It was under my bed.

_____

24. We clapped and cheered. Our team scored a goal.

_____

25. We looked at the stars. Night fell.

_____

26. I wanted strawberry ice-cream. The shop only had vanilla.

_____

27. Joe entered the competition. He won!

_____

28. It was not raining. The sky was full of black clouds.

_____

29. The woman sat down for a rest. Her shopping bags were heavy.

_____

30. I told her the secret. I trusted her.

_____

/30

Progress report

Colour each box in the correct colour to show how many questions you got right.

0%–20% = yellow, 21%–50% = green, 51%–70% = blue, 71%–100% = red

This will help you to monitor your progress.

Test 1 /50 % Date _____	**Test 2** /40 % Date _____	**Test 3** /50 % Date _____	**Test 4** /45 % Date _____	**Test 5** /50 % Date _____

Test 6 /30 % Date _____	**Test 7** /40 % Date _____	**Test 8** /40 % Date _____	**Test 9** /30 % Date _____	**Test 10** /40 % Date _____

Test 11 /40 % Date _____

Test 12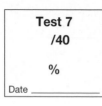

Test 13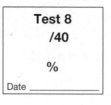

Test 14 /30 % Date _____

Test 15 /30 % Date _____

Test 16 /40 % Date _____	**Test 17** /40 % Date _____	**Test 18** /50 % Date _____	**Test 19** /40 % Date _____	**Test 20** /40 % Date _____

Test 21 /35 % Date _____

Test 22

Test 23

Test 24 /30 % Date _____

Test 25 /60 % Date _____

Test 26 /40 % Date _____	**Test 27** /40 % Date _____	**Test 28** /30 % Date _____	**Test 29** /50 % Date _____	**Test 30** /30 % Date _____